Music Theory Practice Papers 2018

ABRSM's *Music Theory Practice Papers 2018* are based on the 2018 Music Theory exam papers. The questions are the same as those used in recent exams.

Find out more about our Music Theory exams at **www.abrsm.org/theory**.

Theory Paper   Grade 4   2018   A

Duration 2 hours

TOTAL MARKS
100

This paper contains SEVEN questions, ALL of which should be answered.
Write your answers on this paper – no others will be accepted.
Answers must be written clearly and neatly – otherwise marks may be lost.

1   Look at this melody and then answer the questions below.

15

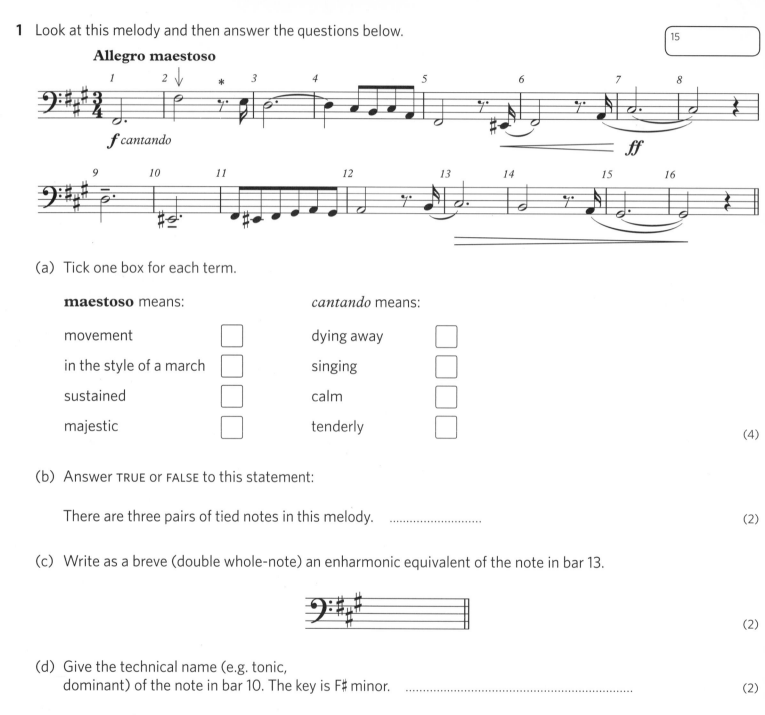

(a)   Tick one box for each term.

maestoso means:		*cantando* means:	
movement	☐	dying away	☐
in the style of a march	☐	singing	☐
sustained	☐	calm	☐
majestic	☐	tenderly	☐

(4)

(b)   Answer TRUE or FALSE to this statement:

There are three pairs of tied notes in this melody.   ....

(2)

(c)   Write as a breve (double whole-note) an enharmonic equivalent of the note in bar 13.

(2)

(d)   Give the technical name (e.g. tonic, dominant) of the note in bar 10. The key is F♯ minor.   ....

(2)

(e)   How many demisemiquavers (32nd notes) is the **rest** in bar 2 (marked ∗) worth?   ....

(2)

(f)   Rewrite the first note of bar 2 (marked ↓) so that it sounds at the same pitch, but using the alto clef.
      Remember to put in the clef and the key signature.

(3)

2 (a) Describe fully (e.g. minor 3rd, perfect 4th) each of these melodic intervals.

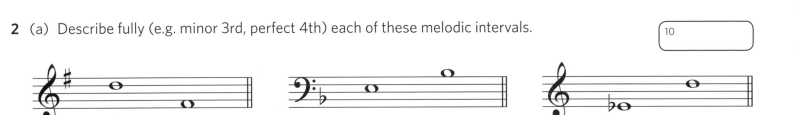

....

(b) **After** each of these notes write a **higher** note to form the named **melodic** interval.

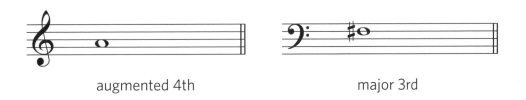

augmented 4th   major 3rd

3 (a) Write one octave **ascending** of the scale of F **harmonic** minor. Do **not** use a key signature but put in all necessary accidentals. Use semibreves (whole notes) and begin on the tonic.

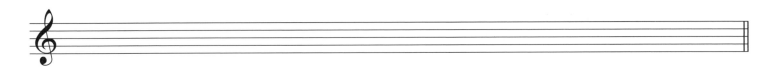

(b) Add the correct clef and any necessary accidentals to make the scale of B major. Do **not** use a key signature.

4 Look at this melody by Mozart and then answer the questions that follow.

(a) (i) Name the two ornaments marked **X** and **Y**.

10

   X (bar 3) .... (2)

   Y (bar 9) .... (2)

   (ii) Give the number of a bar that contains
   all the notes of the tonic triad of E♭ major.   Bar .... (2)

   (iii) Complete the following statement:

   All the notes in bars 10–12 can be found in the key of .... major. (2)

   (iv) Give the letter name of the **highest** note in the melody.   .... (2)

(b) (i) Rewrite bar 11, without the ornament, using notes and a rest of **twice the value**. Remember to put in the new time signature.

(4)

(ii) Compare bars 1−2 with bars 4−6 (both marked ⌐‾‾‾‾⌐) and then name one similarity and one difference.

Similarity .... (1)

Difference .... (1)

(iii) Answer TRUE or FALSE to this statement:

The melody begins with an upbeat. .... (2)

(iv) Underline **one** word from the list below that has a similar meaning to **Allegro**.

assez   *vite*   *avec*   *douce* (2)

(c) (i) Name a standard orchestral woodwind instrument, which normally uses the treble clef, that could play this melody so that it sounds at the same pitch.

.... (2)

(ii) Name the highest-sounding member of the standard orchestral brass family. .... (2)

(iii) Name the lowest-sounding member of the standard orchestral string family. .... (2)

(iv) Underline **two** instruments from the list below that are members of the standard orchestral percussion family.

bassoon   timpani   bass drum   viola (4)

7

5 Transpose this melody **down an octave**, using the bass clef as shown.

10

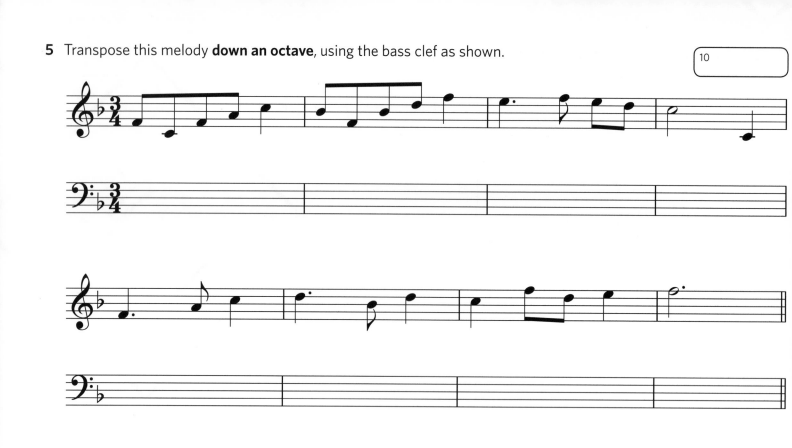

6 Add the correct rest(s) at the places marked ∗ in these two melodies
to make each bar complete.

10

7 (a) Name each of the numbered chords as tonic (I), subdominant (IV) or dominant (V).
The key is B♭ major.

Hymn Tune, 'Unser Herrscher'

Chord:

(1) ....

(2) ....

(3) ....   (6)

(b) Identify these triads by naming the key and describing them as tonic (I), subdominant (IV)
or dominant (V).

Key ....   Key ....   Key ....

Triad ....   Triad ....   Triad ....

(9)

Theory Paper   Grade 4   2018   B

TOTAL MARKS
100

Duration 2 hours

This paper contains SEVEN questions, ALL of which should be answered.
Write your answers on this paper – no others will be accepted.
Answers must be written clearly and neatly – otherwise marks may be lost.

1   Look at this melody and then answer the questions below.

15

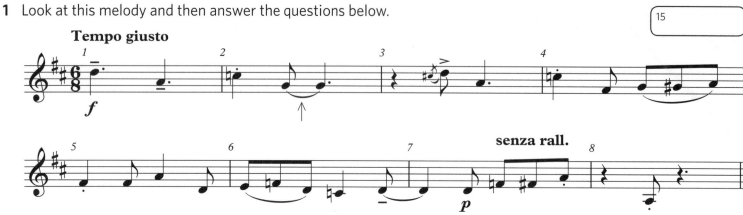

(a) Tick one box for each term.

Tempo giusto means:		**senza rall.** means:	
with some freedom of time	☐	getting faster	☐
at the same speed	☐	without getting slower	☐
in strict time	☐	held back	☐
first time	☐	slow	☐

(4)

(b) Name the ornament in bar 3.   ....   (2)

(c) Rewrite bar 4 in simple time but without changing the rhythmic effect.
     Remember to put in the new time signature.

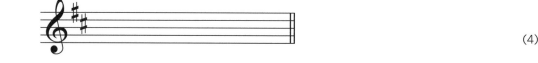

(4)

(d) How many semiquavers (16th notes) are the
     tied notes in bar 2 (marked ↑) worth in total?   ....   (2)

(e) Give the letter name of the **lowest** note in the melody.   ....   (1)

(f) Write as a breve (double whole-note) an enharmonic equivalent of the first note of the melody.

(2)

2 (a) Describe fully (e.g. minor 3rd, perfect 4th) each of these melodic intervals.

....

(b) **After** each of these notes write a **higher** note to form the named **melodic** interval.

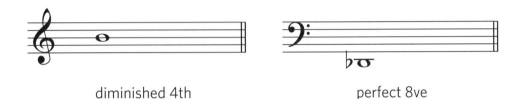

           diminished 4th   perfect 8ve

3 (a) Write one octave **ascending** of the scale of A♭ major. Do **not** use a key signature but put in all necessary accidentals. Use semibreves (whole notes) and begin on the tonic.

(b) Write the key signature of G♯ minor and then one octave **descending** of the **harmonic** minor scale. Use semibreves (whole notes), begin on the tonic and remember to put in any necessary accidentals.

4 Look at this melody by Haydn and then answer the questions that follow.

(a) (i) Give the technical name (e.g. tonic, dominant) of
the last note in bar 1 (marked *). The key is F major. .... (2)

(ii) Underline **one** word from the list below that has a similar meaning to **assai**.

avec   *très*   *cédez*   *lent*   (2)

(iii) Tick one box for this term.

Vivace means:

slow ☐

lively, quick ☐

gradually getting quicker ☐

at a medium speed ☐

(2)

(iv) Rewrite bars 3–4 **an octave lower**, using the bass clef as shown.

(4)

(b) (i) Answer TRUE or FALSE to these statements: | 10 |

   All the notes in bar 3 can be found in the scale of G major.   .... (2)

   The sign meaning 'forced, accented' occurs six times in this melody.   .... (2)

(ii) Rewrite bar 6 using notes of **twice the value**. Remember to put in the new time signature.

   (4)

(iii) Give the number of a bar that contains **three** notes
       next to each other that form part of a chromatic scale.   Bar .... (2)

(c) (i) Name two standard orchestral instruments, one string and one woodwind, that could | 10 |
         play this melody so that it sounds at the same pitch.

   String   .... (2)

   Woodwind   .... (2)

(ii) Name the lowest-sounding member
      of the standard orchestral brass family.   .... (2)

(iii) Name two standard orchestral percussion instruments, one that produces sounds of
       definite pitch and one that produces sounds of indefinite pitch.

   Definite pitch   .... (2)

   Indefinite pitch   .... (2)

5 (a) Rewrite this melody with the notes correctly grouped (beamed).

(b) Describe the time signature as: simple or compound   ....

duple, triple or quadruple   ....

6 (a) Rewrite these bass-clef notes at the same pitch but using the alto clef.

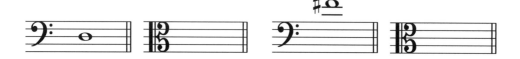

(b) Rewrite these alto-clef notes at the same pitch but using the treble clef.

14

7 (a) Name each of the numbered chords as tonic (I), subdominant (IV) or dominant (V). The key is E minor.

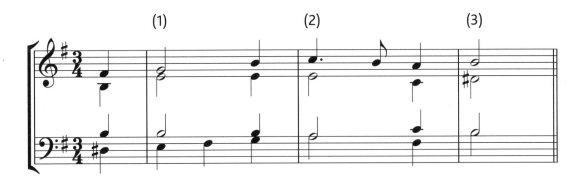

Chord:

(1) ....

(2) ....

(3) ....   (6)

(b) Write the key signatures and triads named below.

      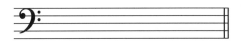

Bb minor   F# minor   Bb major
tonic   dominant   subdominant

(9)

Theory Paper   Grade 4   2018   C

TOTAL MARKS
100

Duration 2 hours

This paper contains SEVEN questions, ALL of which should be answered.
Write your answers on this paper – no others will be accepted.
Answers must be written clearly and neatly – otherwise marks may be lost.

1   Look at this melody and then answer the questions below.

15

(a) Tick one box for each term.

Tempo comodo means:		*morendo* means:	
slow, stately	☐	dying away	☐
first time	☐	becoming more lively	☐
at a comfortable speed	☐	calm	☐
in time	☐	hurrying	☐

(4)

(b) Rewrite the last note of the melody so that it sounds at the same pitch, but using the alto clef. Remember to put in the clef and the key signature.

(3)

(c) Complete the following statement:

The triplet (♩ ♩ ♩) in bar 2 means

three crotchets (quarter notes) in the time of ....

(2)

(d) Describe the time signature as: simple or compound   ....

(1)

duple, triple or quadruple   ....

(1)

(e) Answer TRUE or FALSE to this statement:

The rest in the last bar is worth 24 demisemiquavers (32nd notes).   ....   (2)

(f) The melody is in the key of B♭ major.
Which other key has the same key signature?   ....   (2)

2 (a) Describe fully (e.g. minor 3rd, perfect 5th) each of these harmonic intervals.   [10]

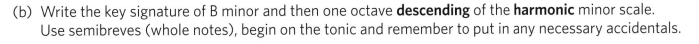

....

(b) **Above** each of these notes write a **higher** note to form the named **harmonic** interval.

perfect 5th   major 6th

3 (a) Add the correct clef and any necessary accidentals to make the scale of D♭ major.   [10]
Do **not** use a key signature.

(b) Write the key signature of B minor and then one octave **descending** of the **harmonic** minor scale.
Use semibreves (whole notes), begin on the tonic and remember to put in any necessary accidentals.

4 Look at this melody by Beethoven and then answer the questions that follow.

(a) (i) Underline **one** word from the list below that has a similar meaning to **Adagio**.

animé   vite   cédez   lent

(2)

(ii) Name the **two** ornaments marked **A** and **B**.

A (bar 5) ....

(2)

B (bar 7) ....

(2)

(iii) Write as a breve (double whole-note) an enharmonic equivalent of the last note of the melody.

(2)

(iv) Answer TRUE or FALSE to this statement:

Each complete bar has a different rhythm. ....

(2)

18

(b) (i) Give the technical names (e.g. tonic, dominant) of the two notes marked **X** and **Y**.
The key is F major.

10

X (bar 2) .... (2)

Y (bar 6) .... (2)

(ii) Rewrite bars 5–6, without the ornaments, **an octave lower**, using the bass clef as shown.

(4)

(iii) Give the number of a bar that contains **five** notes
next to each other that form part of a chromatic scale.   Bar .... (2)

(c) (i) Name two standard orchestral instruments, one woodwind and one brass, that could
play this melody so that it sounds at the same pitch.

10

Woodwind .... (2)

Brass .... (2)

(ii) Name the lowest-sounding member
of the standard orchestral string family.   .... (2)

(iii) Underline **two** instruments from the list below that might be played 'sul G'.

trombone   bass drum   cello   violin

(4)

5 Rewrite this melody using notes and rests of **twice the value**.
Remember to put in the new time signature.

6 Add the correct rest(s) at the places marked ∗ in these two melodies
to make each bar complete.

7 (a) Name each of the numbered chords as tonic (I), subdominant (IV) or dominant (V).
   The key is F♯ minor.

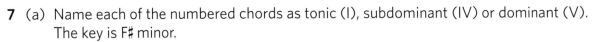

15

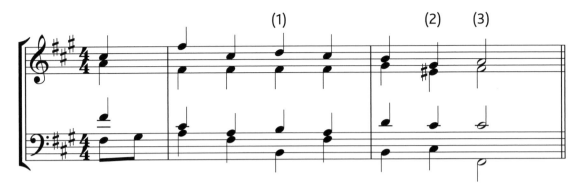

Chord:

(1) ....

(2) ....

(3) ....   (6)

(b) Write the key signatures and triads named below.

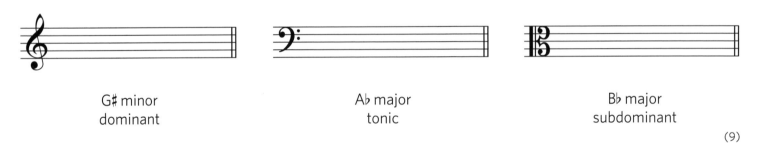

G♯ minor   A♭ major   B♭ major
dominant   tonic   subdominant

(9)

Theory Paper   Grade 4   2018   S

TOTAL MARKS
100

Duration 2 hours

This paper contains SEVEN questions, ALL of which should be answered.
Write your answers on this paper – no others will be accepted.
Answers must be written clearly and neatly – otherwise marks may be lost.

1   Look at this melody and then answer the questions below.

15

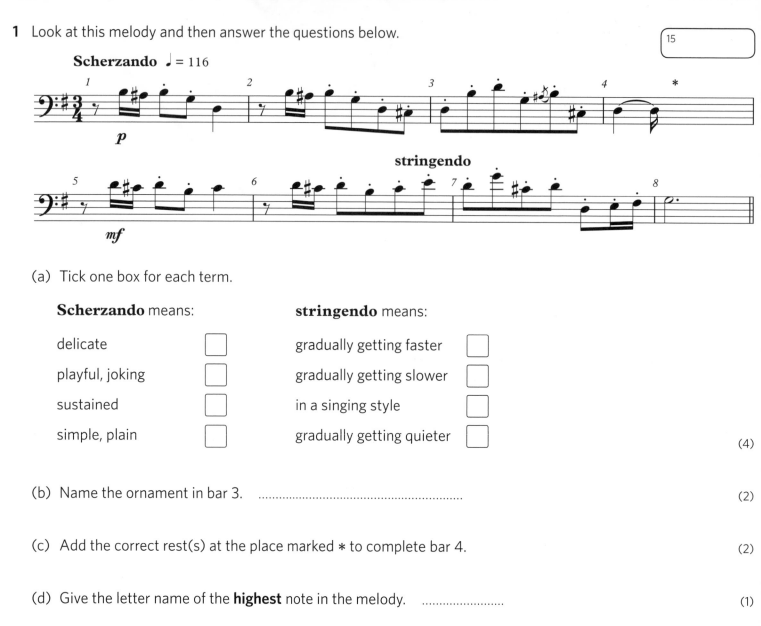

(a) Tick one box for each term.

Scherzando means:		**stringendo** means:	
delicate	☐	gradually getting faster	☐
playful, joking	☐	gradually getting slower	☐
sustained	☐	in a singing style	☐
simple, plain	☐	gradually getting quieter	☐

(4)

(b) Name the ornament in bar 3. ....

(2)

(c) Add the correct rest(s) at the place marked ✳ to complete bar 4.

(2)

(d) Give the letter name of the **highest** note in the melody. ....

(1)

(e) Rewrite bars 7–8 **an octave higher**, using the treble clef as shown.

(4)

(f) Answer TRUE or FALSE to this statement:

♩ = 116 means that there are 116 crotchet (quarter-note) beats in a minute. ....

(2)

2 (a) Describe fully (e.g. minor 2nd, perfect 5th) each of these melodic intervals.

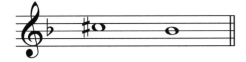
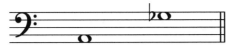

....

(b) **After** each of these notes write a **higher** note to form the named **melodic** interval.

perfect 4th   major 6th

3 (a) Add all necessary accidentals to make a chromatic scale beginning on the given note.

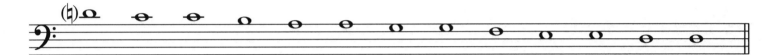

(b) Write one octave **ascending** of the scale of B♭ **melodic** minor. Do **not** use a key signature but put in all necessary accidentals. Use semibreves (whole notes) and begin on the tonic.

4 Look at this melody, which is from a piece by Mendelssohn, and then answer the questions that follow.

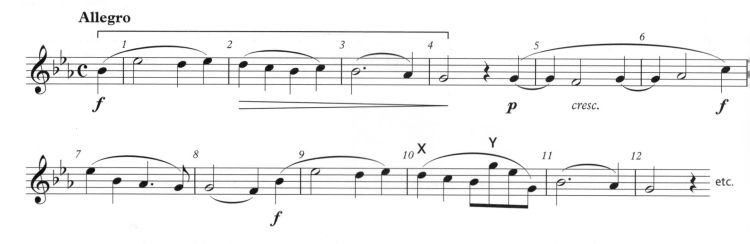

(a) (i) Give the technical names (e.g. tonic, dominant) of the two notes in bar 10 marked **X** and **Y**. The key is E♭ major.

    X .... (2)

    Y .... (2)

(ii) Which other key has the same key signature as E♭ major? .... (2)

(iii) Give the number of a bar that contains **all** the notes of the tonic triad of E♭ major.   Bar .... (2)

(iv) Write as a breve (double whole-note) an enharmonic equivalent of the last note of the melody.

(2)